Life Science Publishing, Pamela Hunter, & Stacey Vann
1.800.336.6308
www.DiscoverLSP.com

Printed in the United States of America
10 9 8 7 6 5 4 3 2 1

Life Science Publishing is the publisher of this book and is not responsible for its content. The information contained herein is for educational purposes only and as a guideline for your personal use. It should not be used as a substitute for medical counseling with a health professional. The authors and publisher do not accept responsibility for such use.

Although the authors and publishers have made every effort to ensure the accuracy of the information contained in this book, we assume no responsibility for errors or omissions.

The essential and supplemental products discussed at length in this book are the sole product of Young Living Essential Oils, LC. The authors and publisher are completely separate entities from Young Living Essential Oils, LC. Products mentioned may be reformulated, discontinued, expanded, or enhanced by Young Living Essential Oils, LC at any given time.

Neither the authors nor the publishers advocate the use of any other essential oils without Young Living Essential Oils, LC's exclusive Seed to Seal® guarantee. Even minor changes in the quality of an essential oil may render it, at best, useless and, at worst, dangerous. The use of essential oils should be done with thorough study, watchful care, and judicious prudence.

Some of the content in this book is derived from the Essential Oils Desk Reference, one of the most widely sought, sold, and read essential oils books of all time. This content is used with written permission from the publisher. Life Science Publishing retains all rights to the content of both the Essential Oils Desk Reference and related volumes in this series.

FOREWORD

Whether this is your first step in living a cleaner, greener, more health-conscious life, or you're a long-time devotee of green living, essential oils are a godsend. They have the power to change people's lives. I happen to know firsthand!

At the age of 21, I was told that I would not live to see 30 because of a serious autoimmune disease. My only chance at survival? Over 15 months of grueling, heartbreaking chemotherapy. It was a long-hard battle—one that I still face every day. And, I couldn't do it without my Young Living Essential Oils.

I'm a long way past 30 (or maybe I've just turned 29 a few times), but I have to say this new lease on life inspired me to make a difference. The past two decades I've devoted myself to the cause of education. But I'm not talking about the make-you-snore-take-a-test-and-forget kind of learning. (Obviously, that has its place. I think...) I'm talking about real knowledge that people can use right away. I'm talking about the self-empowering kind of education, the kind that really frees you to take your life, your health, and your future into your own hands.

In fact, this volume and its many companion volumes are the perfect way to get not only acquainted with essential oils and their many uses, but to do something with them right away. Today, in fact. Every year, my team and I search for the best, most updated information and scientific studies to continue building practical education tools for people to use. It has become an ongoing labor of love and a personal passion. I firmly believe that education is the key to improving the health and lives of everyone in this world. I'm particularly proud of the work Pamela and Stacey have done to share with you the important information in this volume about a fuller mind-body connection.

My company, Life Science Publishing, has been around since Young Living's beginning. While I wasn't there when the doors opened, I certainly know the daily struggles that come with being an entrepreneur. There are constant ups and downs. I can't say they are easy, but I would say they are worth it. I have turned to great mentors in my life, and I believe we can all learn from someone who has been in our shoes before.

Now, I'm not here to sell you oils. I'm here to invite you to learn the simple, practical ways they can make a difference in your life—and the lives of the loved ones around you. I'm here to help you get introduced to oils and help you learn how to put them into your own homemade recipes and solutions. The steps that Pamela & Stacey provide help you to take immediate action—to put yoga techniques into practice right away.

I would love to say we've met, but if all you know of me is the picture in this book, I hope to meet you soon! I've been told that my energy and passion are contagious. If that's the case, I hope you catch them both…

Love. Learn. Share.

xoxo

Troie Battles

Troie Storms-Battles

ABOUT THE AUTHORS

Pamela Hunter and Stacey Vann have been teaching yoga together since 1999 and experiencing Young Living Essential Oils since 2002. Pamela & Stacey are members of the faculty for Young Living Essential Oils: Balance Yoga and Wellness Retreats offered around the globe.

Founder of Fun Lovin' Wellness, Pamela Hunter believes in awakening awareness and opening paths. Pamela's journey has inspired her and many others to learn and share self-care practices. Pamela creates community through her love and education as a leader for Young Living Essential Oils sharing "little bottles of love." She has taught yoga since 2001 and is E-RYT 500, CYKT, a Certified UZIT (Urban Zen Integrative Therapy) and Internationally respected Integrative Health Coach. She is also certified in several mindful modalities: Clinical Aromatherapy, Spiritual Healing, Reiki, and Reflexology. She is the author of Rise & Shine: 6 Master Steps to Get Moving. She resides in Chicago area with her husband. Her two grown sons are in college. Pamela is traveling, teaching retreats and workshops, writing, and still growing!

www.FunLovinWellness.com

"We transform our body and our mind to meet our soul."
— Pamela Hunter

ABOUT THE AUTHORS

Stacey Vann, E-RYT 500 began teaching yoga in 1997 and started her journey with Young Living in 2002. She weaves and shares the transformative and integrative path of yoga, sound, and Young Living essential oils in the United States and internationally. Stacey's teaching style is infused with laughter, energy, and love. She encourages her students to attain wellness, joy, and connection with a commitment to daily practice, self-care, and an attitude of gratitude. Stacey Vann is a mother, Life Coach, doula, reflexologist, Young Living essential oil educator and founder of the Mahabhuta Yoga Festival, co-founder of Galactic Child Yoga, and is co-owner of Breathe Yoga and Wellness Center where she leads 200 & 300-hour teacher training programs in Pensacola, Florida.

www.StaceyVann.com

"Breathe Deeply, Move Freely, & Live Joyfully."
— Stacey Vann

TABLE OF CONTENTS

TREES: OUR MEDITATION GUIDE

Allow the trees to be your guides on the path to a daily meditation practice.

Start small like the seed. Begin with 3-5 minutes a day. Meditate in a space that is quiet, cozy, and warm. Connect to the comfort and support of the earth. You are loved. Be content that this is the perfect point to begin.

As the seed sprouts and reaches toward the heavens, so will your desire to seek solace in silence and spending time with yourself. You will notice that the body needs support in order for the spine to be straight. The sprout stage is the most delicate. The sprout is steadying the roots, establishing the trunk, and reaching upward. The physical body also needs to be steady and established. The body requires movement to be able to be still in meditation for longer periods of time. The physical practice of yoga is a moving meditation that prepares you for the practice of becoming still in seated or supine meditations.

The trunk of the tree is becoming sturdy and stable like your mind as you cultivate your meditation practice. It takes time for a tree to grow a sturdy trunk. Savor the process. Allow the meditation practice to become consistent and enjoyable as the body is becoming stronger and the mind is becoming peaceful. Come into present time and enjoy every moment with yourself, witnessing the beauty all around you.

The branches and the leaves on the tree are taking form. There is a special relationship between trees and humans. Trees produce the oxygen that we need to breathe, while we, humans, exhale carbon dioxide on which trees thrive.

The beauty of meditation is the connection to breath. Concentration is the key. Concentration is the ability to focus on a single point, while meditation is the ability to focus on all points at once. Focus on each inhale and exhale. You are becoming still and letting go of the mind chatter.

The fruit of meditation is the moment we connect to our highest self with compassion, understanding, and wisdom. We cannot strive to pick the fruit before it is ready. The process occurs naturally, without force, without expectation. The fruit gently releases from the tree ready for us to taste the juiciness of life. It takes many years for a tree to grow into full maturity with the ability to bear fruit. Approach your meditation practice with the same patience as planting the seed of a fruit tree. Both require nourishment, a healthy environment, and loving care.

"True concentration is an unbroken thread of awareness."

— BKS Lyengar

WHAT IS MINDFUL MEDITATION?

Mindful Meditation is awareness. It is awareness of your breath, physical sensations of the body, emotions, mind, and environment. It is a deeper concentration with the focus on self-inquiry and self-knowledge. Concentration is the ability to focus on one point. Meditation is the ability to focus on all points at once. Mindful Meditation is the stillness in your mind, while being at ease in your body.

The goal of meditation is truth, consciousness, and bliss. When we establish a meditation practice, one may experience ultimate freedom in the body, mind, and spirit. This is a process. This feeling of oneness or connection to our higher self is often fleeting and temporary. This is why we commit to a daily practice. It is just that – a practice.

WHY PRACTICE MINDFUL MEDITATION?

There are 4 building blocks of consciousness. Linda Gabriel from thoughtmedicine.com states, "There are 4 basic brain wave frequencies and each correlates with a specific state of consciousness. Like sound frequencies, brain waves are measured in Hz, or cycles per second. In general, the slower the frequency of your brain waves, the more relaxed you feel. Meditation, neurofeedback, hypnosis, and guided imagery have all been shown to help people control their brain waves more efficiently for better health, higher performance, and a more positive experience of life."

The four building blocks are: Beta, Alpha, Theta, and Delta Waves.

Beta Waves: 13-30 Hz

Your brain is alert and active, and also can be associated with over-thinking and worry. You need beta waves in order to think and function consciously with all five external senses, logical mind, memory from the five senses, and logical thinking. Relaxing shifts you into alpha.

Alpha Waves: 8-13 Hz

Your brain is relaxed, day dreamy and in a detached awareness.
Linda expresses, "If you're like most people, when you close your eyes and take a few slow, deep breaths, you'll experience a light, relaxed alpha state. Alpha is considered the gateway to meditation." Alpha brain waves are the state when the stress hormones go down. At the beginning of sleep, you shift from alpha waves to theta waves.

Theta Waves: 4-8 Hz

Your brain is in a deep state of meditation where you experience higher states of consciousness and a high state of mental concentration. This is where we tap into our creative visualization, intuition, and inner guidance. Theta is when we are dreaming and you experience rapid eye movements (REM sleep).

Delta Waves: up to 4 Hz

Your brain is in deep dreamless sleep. This is where you feel you are sleeping like a baby. You are in a deeply relaxed state of oneness.

The brain's frequency changes during various states of awareness and meditation. *We practice Mindful Meditation to experience the shift from beta waves to integrate the benefits of alpha, theta, and delta waves for our brain and our body.*

Practicing may also help us:

- Connect to our breath and our body
- Feel relaxed and blissful
- Access creativity and intuition
- Support a healthy night's rest
- Foster clear thinking
- Feel happiness and joy
- Enhance emotional stability and emotional intelligence
- Experience consciousness to discover our truth
- Develop self-care
- Support overall wellness

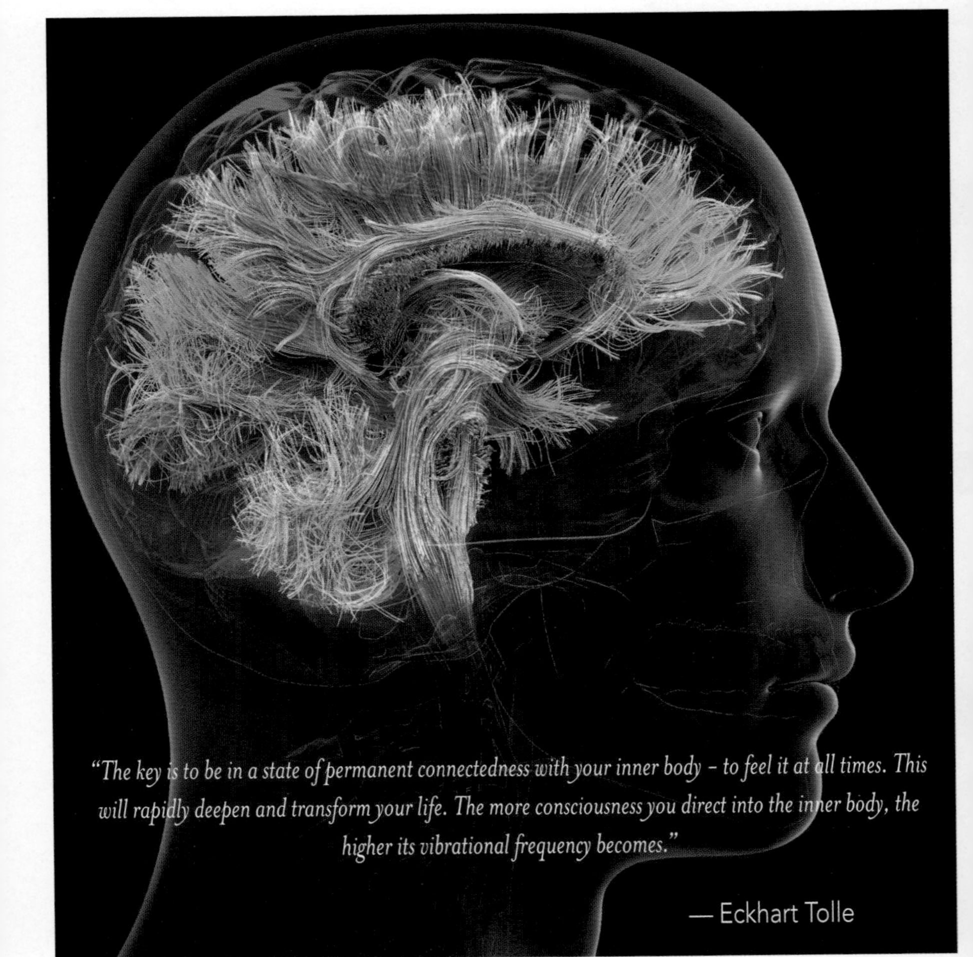

MINDFUL MEDITATION GUIDELINES

1. When to Meditate

Anytime that works for you. The effects are more potent if your practice is the same time every day. Keep in mind practicing first thing in the morning is a wonderful way to start your day. In the evening, at sunset or just before going to bed, is also a good time.

2. Where to Meditate

Choose a place you will not be disturbed or get distracted. Find a space where you can feel at ease, calm, and settled. It is nice to have your seat lifted higher than your knees in a seated position. Consider investing in a yoga blanket, bolster, and/or meditation cushion. But know, it is not necessary to have anything extra but yourself. The priority here is to make the time to be still. Some of our favorite places to meditate are in bed, in nature, in church, and in the after school line waiting to pick up our kids.

3. Commit to Meditate

Whatever meditation you choose to do, in order to get the maximum benefit, it is best to fully commit to doing it for a certain amount of days and length of time. Keep in mind that 3 minutes a day is more effective than 31 minutes once a week. If you do miss a day, don't beat yourself up, start again and keep up!

Committing to a personal practice makes the meditation process of transformation and self-discovery your own. To experience the effects of a meditation, practice daily. This will develop a life-promoting habit. Choose a meditation that suits your goals and/or inspires you, and commit to practicing it over 40, 90, 120, or 1,000 days.

- 40 days: Change a habit.
  - 90 days: Confirm the habit.
    - 120 days: You are the new habit.
      - 1,000 days: Mastery of the new habit.

"The most powerful benefits of meditation come from having a regular, daily practice."

— Deepak Chopra

4. Envision

Take a moment to drop in to this time you are willing to give to yourself. Listen and connect with your breath. Receive the messages. Envision your heart's desires at this moment. See it in your mind's eye and feel it manifested. Sit.

5. Focus For Your Eyes

Your eyes move more than you are aware. During meditation it is recommended to focus the eyes in different positions to allow the mind to quiet.

Focusing at the brow point at the center of the forehead, a little above the eyebrows with closed eyes, corresponds to our higher wisdom and intuition. The focus on the brow point stimulates the pituitary gland and central nerve channel of the spine.

Focusing at the tip of the nose with eyes slightly crossed, balances the left, right, and central nerve channels of the spine. The focus on the tip of the nose stimulates the pineal gland and frontal lobe of the brain, which controls the mind.

Focusing at the tip of the chin with closed eyes rolled downwards to the center of the chin produces a cooling and calming effect.

Focusing at the top of the head with closed eyes rolling upwards, as if looking through the very top, center of the head stimulates the pineal gland.

6. Affirmations

Repetition of words, sounds, or phrases provides a focus for the mind while meditating. The human voice is a powerful instrument for healing and transformation. The sounds you voice vibrates throughout the entire body. Sound travels efficiently through water. The human body is over 70% water, an excellent conductor for sound and vibration. Affirmations may quiet the mind, and may help bring positive changes within. When words or phrases are repeated mentally, no one can see what you are doing; therefore, you can practice anywhere.

7. Being the Witness

The moment you begin observing the fluctuations of your mind, a higher level of mindfulness becomes activated. You then begin to realize that there is a vast realm of intelligence beyond thought, that thought is only a tiny aspect of that intelligence.

"You also realize that all the things that truly matter -- beauty, love, creativity, joy, inner peace -- arise from beyond the mind. You begin to awaken."

— Eckhart Tolle

WHAT ARE ESSENTIAL OILS?

Essential Oils are volatile liquids distilled from roots, stems, leaves, flowers, bark or resin of plants. They are the life energy of the plant kingdom. This life energy extends the wellness and life of the plant.

Essential Oils are potent, highly complex and concentrated substances containing anywhere from 80 – 300 chemical compounds serving the plant for optimum wellness.

Essential Oils are versatile in use. You can turn to them for a variety of needs to support you and keep you above the wellness line (the wellness line is an imaginary line we draw between health issues and optimum wellness).

Essential Oils are also versatile in their application and can be used in these methods:

Inhalation

Simply breathing in essential oils is amazing! The sense of smell is the only sense that travels directly to the brain. The essential oil aroma travels through the olfactory bulb to the Limbic brain where memory and emotions are stored.

Diffusing, Scent Tent, Cotton Pad, and Direct from the Bottle are ways we will use the inhalation method during our Breathing Practices.

Topical

The intelligence of essential oils is fascinating! Applying neat or diluted, directly to a location enhances the physical, mental, emotional, and spiritual awareness in the body.

The bottom of the feet is said to be the safest place to apply topically. The essential oils have their own intelligence and travel where they are needed in the body.

There are various topical applications we will be demonstrating for our Breathing Practices.

Internally

Overall wellness support is brilliant! Young Living Essential Oils has an entire line of Vitality Essential Oils to be used as dietary supplements. Vitality Oils support the systems of the body for overall wellness. When using the topical application for our Breathing Practices, if there is Vitality Oil that matches the topical oils you are using, it is also supportive to our body systems.

WHY PRACTICE MINDFUL MEDIATIONS?
WITH ESSENTIAL OILS

Essential Oils are a simple, safe, and effective addition to Mindful Meditations. They magnify the benefits listed earlier. The synergistic blend of applying essential oils to the body while meditating supports optimum wellness and balance. When you practice these meditations adding essential oils, you may feel your truth, consciousness, and bliss at even a higher frequency!

Each Young Living Essential Oil, based on its complex composition, carries sacred frequencies of nature's living energy. People typically experience a deeper sense of awareness, connectedness, and peace while they meditate with the application of Young Living Essential Oils.

Young Living Essential Oils and meditation are supportive tools for the manifestation of our harmonious physical, mental, emotional, and spiritual well-being. Together the frequencies can stimulate and resonate the cells in the human body and restore the natural flow of your life energy.

Asthmatic Caution:
When using essential oils for breathing practices, please apply your oils as far away from the lungs as possible. Use caution with Lavender.

BASIC GUIDELINES FOR SAFE USE

STORAGE	CAUTIONARY USE	Application
Store in amber bottles	Oils rich in menthol (peppermint) are not suggested to be used on neck or throat area of children < 18 months	Topically apply oils to bottoms of feet or use in bath water, no more than 10 drops
Capped tightly	Citrus oils, Bergamot are photosensitive. Stay out of sun, 1-2 days after application or cover usage area.	Direct inhalation of oils, up to 10-15 times daily
Keep in cool location, out of light	Keep essential oils from eyes and ears. Do not touch eyes, glasses, or contact lenses.	Inhalation of oils not recommended for asthmatics
Keep out of reach of children	People exhibiting chronic, pre-existing health conditions (epilepsy, hypertension, i.e.) should consult physician before use. Particular caution with high ketone oils such as, Basil, Rosemary, Sage, and Tansy oils.	Before internal ingestion, try dilution in Blue Agave, Yacon syrups, or olive or coconut oils, rice milk
Keep vegetable oil on hand for dilution (V-6 Oil complex, other veggie oils)	Pregnant women or people exhibiting allergies should consult their physicians prior to use. Dilution of oils with a vegetable-based oil suggested. Skin patch test on the underside of the arm for 30 minutes warranted. Use common sense.	Reactions to essential oils, topically or by ingestion, may be delayed 2-3 days after use

FEELING THE BREATH

All you need is your breath and your desired essential oil. Feeling the Breath can be done anywhere at anytime for any length of time desired.

Stop what you are doing and notice how you are breathing. Observe. How are you feeling right now?

Bring your attention to your breath. No need to change or manipulate your breath, only observe. Notice how it feels in your body. Is the breath cool or warm? Is the breath long or short? Is the mind calm, or is there a stream of thoughts?

Notice. As the breath leaves the body, notice each part of this experience. When the breath is long, notice that the breath is long. When the breath is short, notice that the breath is short. At any time, add in your essential oil. How does it deepen your connection to your breath?

If (and when) there are thoughts that glide into your mind, allow the thoughts. Acknowledge them, release them, "tell them you will talk to them later" and then gently turn your attention back to the physical sensations of the breath. This is a process. Be with it, allow it, and release the thoughts without judgment as you return to your breath. It's fun, play with it.

You are toning your meditation muscles. Sometimes thoughts will drift for a while before you recognize it. That's ok. Gently bring it back. You are becoming one with your breath. You are feeling your breath and overcoming the obstacles of mind chatter and placing yourself back on track. Over time you will notice your mind becoming more clear. It will become calmer and the experience of Feeling the Breath will bring enhanced wellness.

Add essential oils to this practice easily and simply by:

1. Diffusing
2. Dripping 3 drops of an oil on a cotton pad to inhale when desired
3. Apply 1-3 drops in the palm of your hand, rub your hands together 3x clockwise. Bring your hands to your nose in a Scent Tent and inhale when desired.

Our Favorite Young Living Essential Oils for ***Feeling the Breath***:
Pick one and connect with it.

- Breathe Again™
- Frankincense
- Juniper
- Myrtle
- Orange
- Present Time™
- Reconnect™
- Surrender™
- Eucalyptus Globulus
- Grounding™
- Lemon
- Northern Lights Black Spruce
- Pine
- Raven™
- Release™

BELLY BREATHING (ABDOMINAL BREATH)

From a seated or supine (laying down) position, start by exhaling out through the nose and bringing your abdomen gently back towards the spine releasing all of your air. On the inhalation, as you breathe in through your nose, relax the abdomen, it will naturally rise and fill like a big balloon. When you exhale again, your belly will deflate. It may help to place your palms or a stuffed animal on the abdomen in order to feel the movements of the breath. Continue breathing until you have established a natural rhythm. Inhale; you'll feel the belly rise and fill up like a big balloon. Exhale; you'll feel the belly fall and deflate the balloon. If the breathing muscles are tight, it can be helpful to practice this breath in a supine position with a bolster under the knees to relax.

In order to breathe deeply and expand your lung capacity, let's review the science of the breath. Ideally, the diaphragm contracts downward, and the belly will expand with oxygen. To expel the carbon dioxide, the diaphragm relaxes upward, compressing the lungs and expelling the air out; this causes the belly to sink. The abdominal region is very tight when you are under stress. The abdomen is a nice place to apply 1-3 drops of your Young Living Essential Oil during Belly Breathing.

Our Favorite Young Living Essential Oils for ***Belly Breathing***:

- AromaEase™
- Fennel
- Gathering™
- Harmony™
- InnerChild™
- Purification™
- Digize™
- Forgiveness™
- Ginger
- Humility™
- Oola®*Family™
- Transformation™

"Our breath, like our heartbeat, is the most reliable rhythm in our lives. When we become attuned to this constant rhythm, our breath can gradually teach us to come back to the original silence of the mind."
— Donna Farhi

**Oola is a registered trademark of OolaMoola, LLC*

MINDFUL 4 OILS
Meditation

A nice mindfulness meditation practice derived from Thich Nhat Hahn. Carry 4 Young Living Essential Oils to help you connect with their frequencies. You will be inhaling and/or applying them throughout the day with an affirmation below:

1) Fresh like a flower: Breathing in saying, "I feel fresh." Breathing out saying, "I am a flower."
Some of our favorites to inhale or apply for this affirmation are: *Geranium, Jasmine, Rose, Ylang Ylang.*

2) Solid and firm like a mountain: Breathing in saying, "I feel solid." Breathing out saying, "I am a mountain."
Some of our favorites to inhale or apply for this affirmation are: *Grounding™, Idaho Blue Spruce, Sacred Mountain™, and Valor®.*

3) Still water reflecting: Breathing in saying, "I am the stillness of water." Breathing out saying, " I am reflecting the stillness."
Some of our favorites to inhale or apply for this affirmation are:
Gentle Baby™, Lavender, Peace & Calming™, and Tranquil™.

4) Spaciousness: Breathing in saying, "I feel space inside and around me." Breathing out saying, "I am free."
Some of our favorites to inhale or apply for this affirmation are:
Acceptance™, Freedom™, Joy™, and Present Time™.

AFFIRMATION
Meditation

Choose an affirmation that speaks to you. Connect with your favorite essential oil and enhance the effect of its application while you apply it saying your affirmation. We invite you to be creative and feel your affirmation and oil combo for your self.

Here are some examples of our favorite affirmations and essential oils combos.

1) ***I am beautiful, bountiful, and blissful.*** *Inhale or apply the oil of Abundance™.*

2) ***I am happy and free.*** *Inhale or apply the oil of Joy™.*

3) ***I am love.*** *Inhale or apply the oil of Sacred Frankincense™.*

4) ***I am peace.*** *Inhale or apply the oils of Peace & Calming™.*

PEACE-LOVE-LIGHT-JOY
Meditation

For this meditation, you may desire to dip your fingers into your Young Living Essential Oils of choice. Your eye focus may be at your brow point.

In a comfy position with your hands at your sides or resting in your lap, begin by touching your thumb to your index finger saying aloud or silently – PEACE.

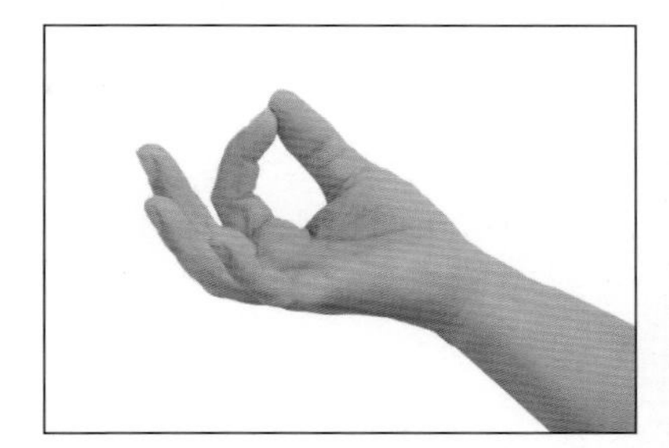

Open the hand, then touch your thumb to your middle finger saying aloud or silently – LOVE.

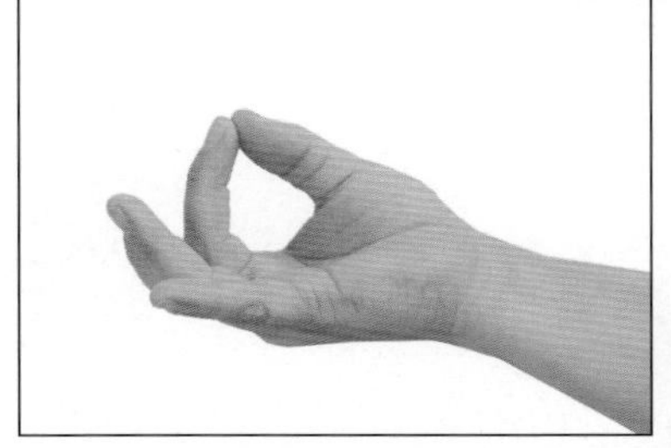

Open your hand, touch your thumb to your ring finger saying aloud or silently – LIGHT.

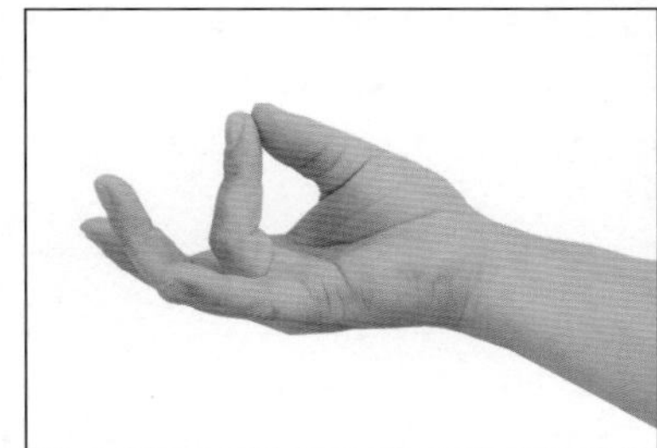

Open your hand, then touch your thumb to your pinky finger saying aloud or silently – JOY. Repeat by going back to your thumb and index finger. We like to practice this aloud for 3 minutes, whisper for 3 minutes, silent for 3 minutes, whisper 3 minutes, and then aloud 3 minutes.

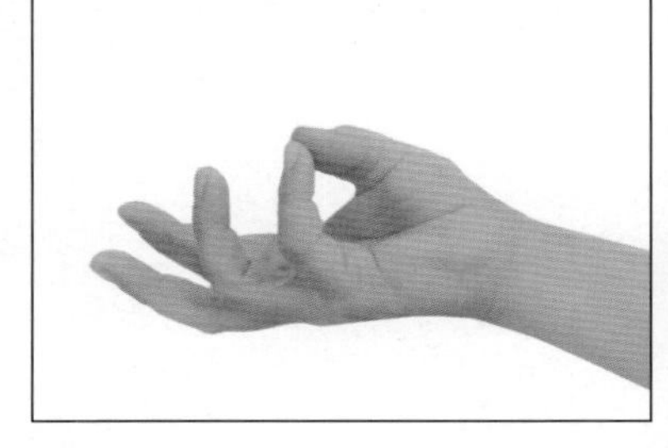

NATURE
Meditation

Nature inspires us. It has the power to shift our whole perspective. As we see and hear nature around us, we sense our spiritual connection. Being in nature lifts you up, calms the busy mind, and brings clarity. There are many natural settings.

"I love the ocean but for something near by, I take a little trek to the woods or sit in my own backyard, watching the birds"

— Stacey Vann

Even if the weather is not optimal, experiencing nature a few minutes a day can make a difference in how you feel and see things. It is a gift.

When walking, first begin to walk briskly for a few minutes. This helps to clear the mind and bring in fresh air with your deeper breaths. Breathe in the freshness and exhale to release stagnation. When ready, slow your pace and begin to take in the nature surrounding you. Observe it all, the ground, the sky, and everything in between. Do not label or think about what you see too deeply. Just notice.

Notice your breath along with the multitude of sensations in your body. Be aware of the sensations on your skin - temperature, clothing, wind, smells, etc.

You can choose to sit in nature rather than walk. You may even choose to kayak or bike. Anything we choose to do can be a form of meditation when we bring mindfulness to it.

When we allow nature to be the center of our practice, we can feel a participation and connection to our Essence. Simply being in nature supports our path to a lifestyle of wellness.

It is beautiful to end this meditation with a few moments of gratitude for our connection to nature.

The beauty of Young Living Essential Oils is, they are gifts from nature. During this Nature Meditation, it is a nice way to honor where our oils come from. May we honor our founder, mentor, and teacher, Gary Young for bringing them to all of us.

Some of our favorite Young Living Essential Oils for Nature Meditation are: Cedarwood, Cypress, Juniper, Marjoram, Idaho Balsam Fir, Idaho Blue Spruce, Sage, Pine, and Northern Lights Blue Spruce.

"Walk as if you are kissing the Earth with your feet."
—Thích Nhat Hanh

LOVING KINDNESS
Meditation

The Loving Kindness Meditation helps us to see goodness and wish happiness for others and ourselves. Many people commit to practicing this meditation on a daily basis. As you continue this meditation, it will carry into daily life—particularly as you find yourself saying it silently, wishing goodness for strangers that you meet.

Below is one example of this ***Loving Kindness Meditation***.

- First, find a quiet place where you can sit or lie without disruption for about 15 minutes.

- To begin, take a few deep gentle breaths to quiet your mind and relax the body.

- Begin by offering Loving Kindness to yourself. If distracting thoughts arise, acknowledge them, allow them to float by like clouds. Then gently bring yourself back to ***Loving Kindness.***

- For yourself say:

  May I be happy. May I be well. May I be at peace.

- Next think of someone close to you that you love.
  Say to yourself...

  May he/she be happy. May he/she be well.
  May he/she be at peace.

- Then choose someone you feel neutral towards.

  May he/she be happy. May he/she be well.
  May he she be at peace.

- Now move to someone that you don't particularly like.

  May he/she be happy. May he/she be well.
  May he/she be at peace.

- Allow your meditation to radiate out further to family, your workplace, where you live, to our country.

  May they be happy. May they be well.
  May they be at peace.

- Finally bring it to everything and everyone in the world.

  May they all be happy. May they all be well.
  May they all be at peace.

- Once the practice is complete, sit still for a few minutes, feeling gratitude for unity and love.

We love to use the *Good Day Protocol* before the ***Loving Kindness Meditation.*** This Protocol is Valor® on your feet, Harmony™ on your navel, Joy™ on your heart, and White Angelica™ on your shoulders. It is such a gift from our founder!

BLESSING YOURSELF & THE WORLD
Meditation

This meditation is a blessing for yourself and the world.

1. Sit in Easy Pose with a straight spine in a seated posture or comfortably in a chair.
2. Apply 1-3 drops of the essential oils of your choice in your palms and take a moment to breathe in the oil. Breathe long, slow, and deep with a feeling of self-love.
3. Close the eyes.
4. Take a moment to meditate on three specific blessings that you are grateful for right now.
5. Bring both your palms facing down, six to nine inches above the top center of your head. Feel the blessings pour into you from the top of the head, down your spine, all the way to you feet.
6. Hold the position for 1-3 minutes.
7. To End: Inhale, Suspend the Breath, Exhale and release your arms with your palms face up on your knees.

Take a moment to bring blessings of wellness, purpose, and abundance to the world.

Our favorite essential oils for ***Blessing Yourself & the World Meditation***:

- Dream Catcher™
- Gathering™
- Humility™
- Live Your Passion™
- White Angelica™
- Fulfill Your Destiny™
- Gratitude™
- Joy™
- Magnify Your Purpose™

RAINBOW
Chakra Meditation

Sit, lie down, or even stand with your feet grounded on the earth. You choose.

Have someone read this meditation to you or voice record yourself saying it to your self so you can listen to it.

Ways to use Young Living Essential Oils for the ***Rainbow Meditation***:

- You may apply 1-2 drops of Harmony around your navel to open up your channels of energy, your chakras.
- You may decide to choose an essential oil for each color, chakra, energy center.
- You may choose to focus on just one color, chakra, or energy center by applying an essential oil to that area of the body.
- You may choose to apply one or many of the essential oils to the bottom of your feet before, during, or after the meditation.

Look for the suggested essential oils list at the end of the meditation.

Feel like there is a waterfall of white light streaming down around you, from the top of your head down your body. It is warm, beautiful, and embracing every inch of your body to the tip of your head to the tip of your toes. This waterfall coming over your Light within, illuminates a prism of beautiful rainbow colors inside you! This rainbow is full of bright, vibrant colors.

Take a deep breath in seeing the color **RED** from your feet to your seat. You see the color red reminding you of the strawberries of the summer, the watermelon, and the sweet red apples in the fall season. You see ruby red roses reminding you of love. When you see that **RED** from your feet to your seat, you are reminded,

"I have. I have all that
I need in my midst.
I have my health.

I have...you complete your sentence."

Your deep breath of warmth keeps this waterfall streaming down around you. You breathe in the color red and it turns to **ORANGE** at your reproductive organs: the color of the gorgeous oranges that are so sweet and juicy, the color orange of sunsets. That color **ORANGE** that reminds you,

"I feel. I feel blessed.
I feel whole.

I feel...you complete your sentence."

With every breath, the waterfall keeps coming down, the prism keeps growing stronger, and the breath keeps coming in with red to orange to **YELLOW** at the solar plexus, just below the navel. Our thoughts takes us to the yellow of the daffodils in the spring, the yellow of lemons we squeeze in our water every morning to alkalize our body, the color yellow of the bright sunshine in the mid-day when we look up and feel so blessed. **YELLOW** at the solar plexus, we are reminded,

"I can. I can have it all.
I can heal myself.

I can...<u>you complete your sentence.</u>"

The waterfall embraces us with white light all around moving into our prism with our breath shining our rainbow in red, orange, yellow, and in to our heart with **GREEN.** The green is all around us with grass and leaves on the trees, the green limes, apples, grapes, and dark leafy green veggies that help us heal. With that color **GREEN**,

"I love. I love myself.
I love others.

I love....
you complete your sentence."

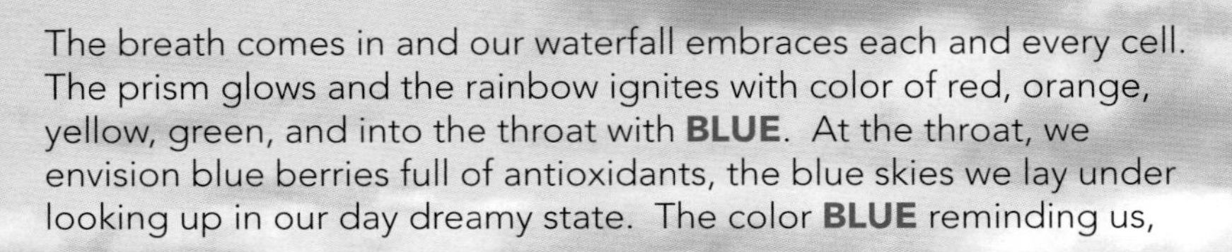

The breath comes in and our waterfall embraces each and every cell. The prism glows and the rainbow ignites with color of red, orange, yellow, green, and into the throat with **BLUE**. At the throat, we envision blue berries full of antioxidants, the blue skies we lay under looking up in our day dreamy state. The color **BLUE** reminding us,

"I speak. I speak truth.
I speak even in silence.

I speak...you complete your sentence."

The waterfall comes down and the rainbow grows with every breath – you're breathing in the red, orange, yellow, green, blue, and **PURPLE** at your third eye. At your third eye, the color purple resonates as we see purple grapes and plums, the beautiful haze in the purple sky at dusk. The color **PURPLE** reminds us,

"I see. I see my glorious life.
I see beautiful people and

God's creations all around me.

I see...you complete your sentence."

The breath gets stronger and stronger and the waterfall and white light comes in breathing red, orange, yellow, green, blue, purple, and **WHITE** light at the crown. With this **WHITE** light – it's glowing all around us now reminding us,

"I am. I am God's child.
I am happy, healthy, and holy.

I am....you complete your sentence."

We feel whole. We feel complete as the waterfall streams down igniting our prism within, protecting us, loving, embracing us, filling us with love and light. Glowing our rainbow to shine forth within us. Bringing us: Red "I have." Orange "I feel." Yellow "I can." Green "I love." Blue "I speak." Purple "I see." White "I am."

Our favorite Young Living Essential Oils for this Rainbow Meditation:

RED – I have –

Abundance™ ~ Black Pepper ~ Cedarwood ~ Cypress ~ Grounding™
Idaho Balsam Fir ~ Patchouli ~ Valor® ~ Vetiver

ORANGE – I feel –

Clary Sage ~ Endoflex™ ~ Geranium ~ InnerChild™
Jasmine ~ Lady Sclareol™ ~ Orange ~ Tangerine ~ Rose
SclarEssence™ ~ Ylang Ylang

YELLOW – I can –

Believe™ ~ Fennel ~ Forgiveness™ ~ Ginger ~ Highest Potential™
Lemon ~ Lemongrass ~ Live Your Passion™ ~ Magnify Your Purpose™
Oregano ~ Peppermint ~ Purification® ~ Thyme

GREEN – I love –

AromaLife™ ~ Believe™ ~ Coriander ~ Eucalyptus Globulus
Eucalyptus Radiata ~ Frankincense ~ Joy™ ~ Marjoram
Rosemary ~ Sacred Frankincense™

BLUE – I speak –

Australian Blue™ ~ Blue Cypress ~ Brain Power™ ~ Clarity™
Idaho Blue Spruce ~ Humility™ ~ Highest Potential™ ~ Valor®

PURPLE – I see –

Copaiba ~ Envision™ ~ Inspiration™ ~ Juniper
Lavender ~ Myrrh ~ Sandalwood

WHITE – I am –

3 Wise Men™ ~ Cedarwood ~ Frankincense ~ Myrrh
Northern Lights Black Spruce ~ Sacred Frankincense™
Sacred Mountain™ ~ Sacred Sandalwood™ ~ White Angelica™

MEDITATING WITH YOUR KIDS

We invite you to practice these meditations with your kids. They are safe, easy, and effective in the same way for children as for adults. Meditating with kids may help them focus their mind, energy, and body movements. It may help them focus and concentrate as a practice during times when they feel scattered or over-stimulated. Teaching children how to meditate is an amazing tool. Overall, teaching children how to sit without interruptions from electronics and life situations is a powerful gift in and of itself.

Thank you for practicing Mindful Meditation with Essential Oils!

An attitude of gratitude is the highest form of prayer. We are grateful for the opportunity to guide you in the practice of mindful meditations with essential oils. Please know that you are your own best guide. Listen to your inner teacher and trust your intuition. All of these meditations are meant to inspire and encourage you to be still and listen. You are exactly where you are meant to be on your personal path to awareness, freedom, and happiness. We have shared these meditations with essential oils to deepen your relationship with your self.

JOURNALING

Which meditation is your favorite?

Which oils and meditation combination(s) speak(s) to you?

What benefits are you experiencing from these meditations?

LEARN MORE...

This is just a whiff of Mindful Breathing with Essential Oils. The oils mentioned are only a fraction of the collection. Talk to your local Young Living member about all of the collection as well as discounts and rewards for using Young Living products.

Join us for a Young Living Balance, Yoga, & Wellness Retreat to get firsthand practice and education about yoga and essential oils.

www.youngliving.com/events

Look for more of our books coming to Life Science Publishers.

SHARE MORE...

Life Science Publishing and Products has everything you need to explore the history, the traditions, the research, the science, and the uses for all essential oils. Visit www.discoverlsp.com to learn how you can make the most of every essential oil single or blend. Whether you need books or tools for your home, glassware for your business, or brochures for helping you share, consider Life Science Publishing and Products your perfect partner.

Content herein derives from the Essential Oil Desk Reference, also owned and published by Life Science Publishing.

Life Science Publishing is the publisher of this handbook. Life Science Publishing is not responsible for its content. The information contained herein is for educational purposes only. It is not provided to diagnose, prescribe, or treat any condition of the body. The information in this handbook should not be used as a substitute for medical counseling with a health professional. Neither the author nor the publisher accepts responsibility for such use.